Two Dogs

by John Shefelbine
Illustrated by Jackie Snider

SCHOLASTIC

Zip and Zap are two dogs.

Zip is little and black.

Zap is big and tan.

Zip has a bed.

His bed is big.

It has a big pad in it.

3

Zap has a bed.

His bed is little.

It has a little pad in it.

4

Zip and Zap are pals.

They like us.

We like them.

Zip and Zap like to run.

We like to run with them.

We all run up a big hill.

Zip gets to the top.

Then Zap gets to the top.

The dogs win!

Zip and Zap see some cats.

They run after them.

The cats run fast.

8

Then the cats run up a  .

Zip and Zap can't get them.

They jump up and down.

9

The dogs are sad.

Then they see some bugs.

They run after the bugs.

10

Chapter 3

Zip and Zap stop and rest.

We sit with them.

Zap naps in the sun.

Where is Zip?

We can't see him.

Is he lost?

12

Zap is sad.

We must look for Zip.

Where did he run?

We see some thick grass.

Is Zip in the grass?

We run up to it.

14

We see a little black thing.

It is little black Zip.

Zip and Zap are glad.

So are we.

My Words

*after	did	it	sad	thick
*some	fast	jump	sit	top
*thing	glad	lost	stop	up
and	grass	must	sun	us
bed	hill	pad	tan	with
big	him	rest	them	Zap
black	in	run	then	Zip

Ss(/z)

bugs	dogs	has	is	pals
cats	gets	his	naps	

-in

win

*new high frequency words